Group Scenes
for
Young Actors

Jessica Penzias

A Beat by Beat Book
www.bbbpress.com

Published by Beat by Beat Press
www.bbbpress.com
Copyright © 2020 by Jessica Penzias

Manufactured in the United States of America

ISBN: 978-0-578-65061-6

—

TABLE OF CONTENTS

SCENES

DAYDREAMING
(5 Actors)

(JAY lays on the ground looking up at the sky happily. DYLAN enters.)

DYLAN: Hey, Jay. What're you doing?

JAY: Daydreaming.

DYLAN: Have you been doing this all day?

JAY: I haven't been paying attention to the time, but yeah, I think I've been up here a while.

DYLAN: Aren't you bored?

JAY: I don't think so.

DYLAN: Well then aren't you lonely? Sitting there all by yourself?

JAY: I'm not alone. I'm with my friend, Porky the porcupine.

(DYLAN notices PORKY who magically appears at JAY's feet.)

PORKY: Hi. I'm Porky.

DYLAN: AH!! Where'd you come from?!

JAY: And I have my memories.

(LITTLE JAY enters looking for something.)

LITTLE JAY: Hi. I'm six-year-old Jay. I lost my sweater at the zoo. Can you help me find it?

DYAN: Woah!! What?! How!?

LITTLE JAY: I don't know how. That's what I'm trying to figure out.

PORKY: I'll help!

1

LITTLE JAY: Thanks!

> *(LITTLE JAY and PORKY wander away, looking for the sweater.)*

JAY: And, of course, I have my future aspirations and dreams.

> *(BIG JAY enters)*

BIG JAY: I am future Jay, and I have just discovered the cure for the common cold!*(BIG JAY sneezes)* *Ah choo!* I think it needs some more work. Back to my laboratory on Mars!

> *(BIG JAY gets to work in their lab, experimenting with different medicines.)*

DYLAN: What's going on!? Where are we!?

JAY: We're in my imagination! Behind the largest waterfall and down the road from the watermelon orchard.

BIG JAY: And also on Mars!

LITTLE JAY: And at the zoo!

DYLAN: Ah! Waterfall! I'm all wet! It's spraying everywhere!

> *(PORKY offers DYLAN a towel.)*

PORKY: Do you want a towel? I weave them out of porcupine quills. Careful. They're sharp.

DYLAN: This doesn't make any sense! Porcupines don't talk and they don't weave!

BIG JAY: Not yet, but in the year 2060 they will. Hey, Little Jay, I found your sweater!

> *(BIG JAY hands LITTLE JAY their sweater.)*

LITTLE JAY: Behind the lions' cage. I shoulda looked there!

PORKY: Hi lions!

DYLAN: Oh no! Lions!

JAY: Oh, don't worry. They're friendly. Anyway, what did you ask me? Oh right! Am I bored? Um, not really. Why? Are you?

- END SCENE -

DOG PARK
(5 Actors)

(LAB, MUTT, CORGI, and BEAGLE play together at the dog park.)

LAB: Stick! Stick! I got the stick!!

(LAB picks up a stick and runs around. The other dogs happily chase LAB.)

MUTT: I want that stick!

CORGI: Ohhhh gimme gimme gimme!

BEAGLE: Doggo, come back here with that stick!

LAB: Mine! Hooray! Hooray! Best day ever! Yes yes yes yes!

(CAT enters.)

CAT: Oooo is that a stick?

MUTT: Who are you?

(MUTT, BEAGLE, and CORGI crowd around CAT. A little ways away, LAB plays with the stick.)

CAT: Hm. I'm not sure. Never really thought about it. Who are *you*!?

MUTT: I'm a dog.

CAT: Cool. I guess I'm a dog too?

BEAGLE: *You* are no doggo. You're a cat.

CAT: I am?

CORGI: What're you doing at the dog park, Cat?

CAT: What're *you* doing here?

MUTT: We're playing with sticks, and chasing balls and birds and stuff.

CAT: Amazing! That's why I'm here too! Wanna play?

BEAGLE: No way! We can't play with no cattos.

(LAB comes over with the stick.)

LAB: What are you all doing over there?

CORGI: This cat says it likes dog stuff.

LAB: That's impossible.

CAT: It is?

CORGI: Yeah. You're a cat. You like chasing yarn and being sort of superior and aloof.

CAT: Yuck. I don't like that any of that. I like squirrels and treats.

ALL DOGS: Treats!? Where!? Where? Treats!?

(The DOGS pant and sniff around looking for treats.)

CAT: Sorry. I don't have any right now.

(LAB puts down the stick and gets closer to CAT.)

LAB: This doesn't make any sense. Why do you like dog stuff?

CAT: Why do you?

LAB: Just do.

CAT: Me too. Why shouldn't I?

LAB: Um, well...

MUTT: ...Huh, I dunno.

BEAGLE: Me either.

CORGI: Well, hmm. I mean I guess you can like whatever you want.

CAT: Say, is this stick taken?

(CAT picks up the stick.)

LAB: Stick!!!

ALL DOGS: Stiiiick!!!

CAT: My stick!

(CAT runs away with the stick. The DOGS chase CAT.)

MUTT: I want that stick!

CORGI: Ohhhh gimme gimme gimme!

BEAGLE: Doggo, come back here with that stick! I mean, catto! I mean - Oh who cares?!

CAT: Mine! Hooray! Hooray! Best day ever! Yes yes yes yes!

- END SCENE -

THE FIGHT
(3 Actors)

(Three siblings – WYATT, TOBIN, and PARKER – sit on the couch watching tv.)

WYATT: Can we watch something else? I don't like this show.

TOBIN: Oh, sorry. I thought you liked it.

PARKER: Me too. What do you wanna watch?

WYATT: I dunno. Something better than this. I don't know how anybody could watch this.

(PARKER passes the remote to WYATT.)

PARKER: Here. You take the remote. You pick.

(WYATT takes the remote, sighs, and turns off the tv.)

TOBIN: Why'd you turn it off?

PARKER: What's wrong?

WYATT: We never fight.

TOBIN: Huh?

WYATT: Other siblings fight. We never fight. Do you think there's something wrong with us?

PARKER: I think we're just in harmony with one another.

TOBIN: Great point! Well said!

PARKER: Thank you!

WYATT: But we can't always be in harmony. It doesn't make any sense! We have to voice our opinions. We have to have conflict!

PARKER: You seem really frustrated. How can I help?

TOBIN: Do you want me to make you a snack?

WYATT: No! I don't want a snack! I want to argue! Don't you two ever disagree with anything I say?

TOBIN: Not usually.

PARKER: Though, I'm not sure I agree with you right now.

WYATT: Good! Let's fight about it!

PARKER: Well, okay. Um... hm... how do I begin? First of all, I understand where you're coming from. You want to improve our relationships and make sure we're being authentic.

TOBIN: You're always looking out for us.

WYATT: Stop appreciating me! You two are terrible at this!

PARKER: Sorry.

TOBIN: Sorry.

WYATT: Ugh!

PARKER: I mean, I'm not sorry? I'm... annoyed?

WYATT: Good. Good. Keep going.

PARKER: I, um, I really like this show, and now we're missing it, all because you want to invent a fight. Well, I don't want to fight! I want to watch!

WYATT: Well, I want to fight!

TOBIN: And I'm indifferent!!

(PARKER continues, getting really into it.)

PARKER: I've been looking forward to this episode all week! This is the season finale! And, all of a sudden, you want to turn off the tv!? Are you out of your mind!? I refuse to miss this just because... because... because... YOU ARE MOODY!

(TOBIN gasps!)

WYATT: I can't believe you just said that. *(Pause.)* That. Was. INCREDIBLE! Some of the best fighting I've ever seen. You got so into it!

PARKER: Thanks. It actually felt pretty good to let it out.

TOBIN: It was sublime. A masterclass, truly.

WYATT: Sorry I made us turn off the tv. I actually hit pause, 'cause I knew you wouldn't want to miss anything.

PARKER: You are so tech savvy! *(WYATT turns on the tv again.)* If you ever want to fight again, just let me know.

WYATT: Will do! Thanks.

TOBIN: I am so proud of us.

- END SCENE -

9

LIBRARY #1
(4 Actors)

(Note: In this version, ASH is played by a girl. See version #2 if ASH is played by a boy.)

(MORGAN and KENDALL study together in the library, while LONDON sits nearby. They scribble silently for a while, then MORGAN speaks in a hushed whisper.)

MORGAN: Can I borrow your eraser?

KENDALL: Here you go.

LONDON: Sh!

MORGAN: Sorry.

(They go back to working. After a moment, KENDALL drums their fingers on the desk.)

LONDON: Sh!

KENDALL: Sorry. I'll stop.

(KENDALL stops drumming their fingers. They continue working in silence. After a moment, LONDON sneezes quietly.)

LONDON: Achoo!

KENDALL & MORGAN: Bless you.

LONDON: Sh!

KENDALL: Seriously?

(They go back to working in silence. ASH enters loudly and speaks to KENDALL and MORGAN.)

ASH: I've been looking for you two everywhere!

LONDON, KENDALL, & MORGAN: Sh!

ASH: Woah. What's the problem?

MORGAN (*whispering*): It's the library. We have to be quiet.

ASH: But, I have news! *(LONDON shoots ASH a scathing look.)* Yikes. Okay. Fine. I won't talk.

> *(For the rest of the scene, ASH, MORGAN, and KENDALL gesture silently to one another like charades. All of the bracketed text is unspoken.)*

KENDALL: [What's your news!?]

MORGAN: [Careful! London's gonna get mad!]

KENDALL: [London's oblivious.]

> *(They look at LONDON who, indeed, appears oblivious, consumed in their work.)*

MORGAN: [Okay. Go ahead. What's the news!?]

ASH: [I got the lead in the school play! I'm going to be Belle!]

KENDALL: [What!?]

MORGAN: [Huh?!]

ASH: [I'm going to be Belle in *Beauty and The Beast*. Beauty. Beast. Beauty. Beast. I'm Beauty!]

KENDALL: [What's she saying?]

MORGAN: [No idea.]

ASH: [I'm going to sing and dance and be the star of the show! I'll read all the books and fall in love with the Beast and save the day!]

KENDALL: [You're sick?]

ASH: [No!]

MORGAN: [You're getting a makeover?]

ASH: [No! Ugh!]

>   *(LONDON slams her book shut.)*

LONDON: Isn't it obvious!? *(MORGAN and KENDALL shake their heads. LONDON speaks loudly and clearly while mimicking the movements Ash just displayed.)* She's going to be the lead in the school play! She's going to be Belle in *Beauty and the Beast*! Beauty. Beast. Beauty. Beast. She's Beauty. She's going to sing and dance and be the star of the show! She'll read books and fall in love with the Beast and save the day!

ASH: [That's it! That's it!]

>   *(ASH, KENDALL, and MORGAN jump up and down in silent celebration.)*

KENDALL & MORGAN: [Yay! Congrats! Hooray!]

LONDON: I gotta find another place to study.

>   *- END SCENE -*

LIBRARY #2
(4 Actors)

(Note: In this version, ASH is played by a boy. See version #1 if ASH is played by a girl.)

(MORGAN and KENDALL study together in the library, while LONDON sits nearby. They scribble silently for a while, then MORGAN speaks in a hushed whisper.)

MORGAN: Can I borrow your eraser?

KENDALL: Here you go.

LONDON: Sh!

MORGAN: Sorry.

(They go back to working silently. After a moment, KENDALL drums their fingers on the desk.)

LONDON: Sh!

KENDALL: Sorry. I'll stop.

(KENDALL stops drumming their fingers. They continue working in silence. After a moment, LONDON sneezes quietly.)

LONDON: Achoo!

KENDALL & MORGAN: Bless you.

LONDON: Sh!

KENDALL: Seriously?

(They go back to working in silence. ASH enters loudly and speaks to KENDALL and MORGAN.)

ASH: I've been looking for you two everywhere!

LONDON, KENDALL, & MORGAN: Sh!

ASH: Woah. What's the problem?

MORGAN (*whispering*): It's the library. We have to be quiet.

ASH: But, I have news! (*LONDON shoots ASH a scathing look.*) Yikes. Okay. Fine. I won't talk.

> (*For the rest of the scene, ASH, MORGAN, and KENDALL gesture silently to one another like charades. All of the bracketed text is unspoken.*)

KENDALL: [What's your news!?]

MORGAN: [Careful! London's gonna get mad!]

KENDALL: [London's oblivious.]

> (*They look at LONDON who, indeed, appears oblivious, consumed in their work.*)

MORGAN: [Okay. Go ahead. What's the news!?]

ASH: [I got the lead in the school play! I'm going to be the Beast!]

KENDALL: [What!?]

MORGAN: [Huh?!]

ASH: [I'm going to be the Beast in *Beauty and The Beast*. Beauty. Beast. Beauty. Beast. I'm the Beast!]

KENDALL: [What's he saying?]

MORGAN: [No idea.]

ASH: [I'm going to sing and dance and be the star of the show! I'll be really scary then fall in love with Belle and become a prince!]

KENDALL: [You're sick?]

ASH: [No!]

MORGAN: [You're getting a pet lion?]

ASH: [No! Ugh!]

(LONDON slams her book shut.)

LONDON: Isn't it obvious!? *(MORGAN and KENDALL shake their heads. LONDON speaks loudly and clearly while mimicking the movements Ash just displayed.)* He's going to be the lead in the school play! He's going to be the Beast in *Beauty and the Beast*! Beauty. Beast. Beauty. Beast. He's the Beast. He's going to be really scary, then fall in love with Belle and become a prince!

ASH: [That's it! That's it!]

(ASH, KENDALL, and MORGAN jump up and down in silent celebration.)

KENDALL & MORGAN: [Yay! Congrats! Hooray!]

LONDON: I gotta find another place to study.

- END SCENE -

NIGHT TIME
(5 Actors)

(TYLER sits up in bed and calls to their parents off-stage.)

TYLER: Goodnight! *(TYLER turns off the light.)* Just close your eyes and go to sleep. You got this.

(ANXIETY enters)

ANXIETY: Did you remember to do all of your homework?

TYLER: What? Uh, yeah. I think so.

ANXIETY: But did you do a good job? Do you think it's perfect? It should be perfect, right? What if it's not perfect?

TYLER: I tried really hard.

ANXIETY: Hard enough?

TYLER: I don't know.

(REGRET enters.)

REGRET: Why did you tell the teacher you were afraid of flying today? That was a pretty weird thing to say. I think she rolled her eyes when you said it.

TYLER: I... I wish I didn't say that.

(FEAR enters.)

FEAR: Airplanes are terrifying! You should be afraid of flying! It's not natural for humans to fly!

(CRITICISM enters.)

CRITICISM: Don't be a wuss. Stop being so scared of everything.

TYLER: Sorry. I -

ANXIETY: Uh oh. You're not sleeping. You should be sleeping. It's getting really late.

TYLER: I'm trying!

ANXIETY: When you don't sleep enough you get sick.

FEAR: Oh no! Not sick! You hate being sick!

REGRET: You didn't sleep last night either. You should have gone to bed earlier.

CRITICISM: Just close your eyes and go to sleep like a normal person!

ANXIETY: Oh no! What if we're not normal?

TYLER: Please! Just let me be! I can't take this!

FEAR: We can't just go away. We're your thoughts! We're always here.

TYLER: But I need a break. I need a break!

CRITICISM: Well, how are you gonna get a break when you can't tame your own mind!? Loser.

TYLER: Hey! That's not a very nice thing to say.

CRITICISM: You thought it!

TYLER: So what? That doesn't make it true!

(Silence.)

ANXIETY: Woah. Good point.

FEAR: I never thought of it that way.

TYLER: I hear you. But I don't have to believe you. And I don't have to answer to you all the time.

FEAR: Where are we supposed to go!?

TYLER: Well, I imagine you'll stick around, but I'm just gonna breathe and rest for a while.

CRITICISM: But you're not good at that! You're so bad at falling asleep!

(TYLER takes a deep breath.)

TYLER *(calmly)*: Okay.

CRITICISM: Did you hear me?

TYLER: I hear you.

CRITICISM: Don't you agree? Shouldn't you worry about it? Or don't you, at least, wanna argue?

TYLER: Nah, I'm good.

CRITICISM: Huh. That's new.

REGRET: I do feel sort of sleepy.

FEAR: I suppose I could use a nap. But I'll be back and I have lots to say!

(TYLER yawns.)

TYLER: I know. That's fine. Goodnight.

ANXIETY: Goodnight.

(They all go to sleep.)

- END SCENE -

YOGA
(5 Actors)

(JAMES, LOTUS, EDEN, and KELLY are students in a yoga class. They sit cross-legged at the front of their mats. Their teacher, DEVON stands before them.)

DEVON: Namaste, everyone. I'm Devon. I'll be your instructor today. I'm excited to guide you through your practice. Yoga is all about bringing yourself into the present moment. We're going to be free and relaxed today.

LOTUS: Namaste.

DEVON: Let's begin on our hands and knees. *(Everyone moves onto their hands and knees.)* Now, I'm going to call out positions and you'll inhabit them fully. We'll start in downward dog. *(Everyone moves into downward dog, with their hands and feet planted on the ground and their hips high.)* Very good. Octopus.

JAMES: Octopus!? I don't know octopus.

KELLY: I'm pretty sure that's not a real pose.

DEVON: Just try to connect with your breath and don't censor yourself.

(EDEN moves into their version of "octopus pose.")

EDEN: I think I'm doing it! Check out my tentacles!

(The other students just sit on their mats and watch EDEN.)

JAMES: I can't do that!

DEVON: Pumpkin.

LOTUS: That is definitely *not* a true asana.

(DEVON shrugs.)

(Once again, EDEN embraces the prompt and becomes a pumpkin, curling up in a ball.)

EDEN: Look, I'm a pumpkin!

KELLY: How do you know that's right?

EDEN: I don't.

(EDEN moves into different poses as Devon calls them out. The other students are frustrated.)

DEVON: Tomato.

JAMES: That's not a pose! It's a vegetable!

EDEN: Technically, tomatoes are fruits. Look, I have seeds! *(EDEN wiggles their fingers as if they are seeds.)* You can do it! C'mon, James.

JAMES: Okay... I'll give it a shot... *(JAMES joins in, embodying a tomato.)* Hey, this is actually pretty fun. Try it!

(LOTUS and EDEN shrug and join in, becoming tomatoes alongside JAMES and EDEN.)

DEVON: Very nice. *(As Devon calls out more poses, the students get more and more into it, each inventing their own versions of the postures.)* Otter.

KELLY: Look. I'm eating seaweed!

DEVON: Book.

LOTUS: This is a real page turner.

DEVON: Poetry.

JAMES: Check it out. I'm "two roads diverging in a wood."

EDEN: Nice!

DEVON: Happiness.
Love.
Peace.
Inhale.
Exhale.*(Everyone takes a deep breath together and smiles contentedly.)* Beautiful work everyone.

- END SCENE -

THE KIDS TABLE
(5 Actors)

(FINLEY, JESS, JULES, YAEL, and SALEM sit around a kitchen table eating dinner together.)

FINLEY: It's an injustice.

JULES: What is?

FINLEY: This!

YAEL: Dinner?

FINLEY: The "kids table." It's an insult.

SALEM: I like the kids table.

FINLEY: Why should we have to sit in the kitchen all alone, eating mac and cheese, while they sit in the dining room, eating fancy food? It's not fair! They just want to keep us out so they can complain about us.

JESS: Oh quiet, Finley. They probably aren't talking about us at all.

FINLEY: Of course they are! Mom and Dad have nothing else to talk about!

JESS: That's not true.

YAEL: Well, even if your parents complain about you, *our* parents would never criticize us!

SALEM: Yeah! Our parents think we're perfect. And Jules' parents wouldn't complain either. Right, Jules?

JULES: I don't know... now I'm nervous.

FINLEY: We should all be nervous! They could be plotting to ground us for eternity or send us off to boarding school!

YAEL: They wouldn't do that.

22

JESS: People don't just sit around whining about kids all the time.

JULES: I think they might!

FINLEY: If we push our ears against the door, we can hear what they're saying.

JULES: Good plan!

FINLEY: Let's go! Come on, Jules.

> *(FINLEY and JULES get up from the table and head towards the exit. JESS calls out after them.)*

JESS: Wait! Don't! *(FINLEY and JULES exit.)* Ugh, Finley is being so paranoid.

YAEL: It's ridiculous!

SALEM: Finley and Jules are both out of control.

JESS: Maybe boarding school isn't such a bad idea... for some people.

YAEL: Seriously.

> *(FINLEY and JULES burst back into the room.)*

FINLEY: I knew it!!

JESS: What are you doing!?

JULES: You *were* talking about us.

YAEL: I thought you were going to eavesdrop on the adults!

FINLEY: We were going to, but then I grew suspicious of the kids table!

JULES *(To FINLEY)*: You were right!

FINLEY: I'm always right! I have never been wrong about this sort of thing.

JESS: Never?

FINLEY: Never.

(They are all silent for a moment and then YAEL panics.)

YAEL: ...I don't want to go to boarding school!

SALEM: They can't ground me!

JESS: Mom! Daaaad!

JULES: We're coming!

(They all exit, running towards the adult table.)

- END SCENE -

THE SPARK
(3 Actors)

(JACKIE and KEATON sit in the school foyer. They huddle over their notebooks and work together. PARIS sits alone nearby.)

KEATON: Oh, that's good. I love that.

JACKIE: I'm writing it down.

KEATON: And then what if we - ?

(PARIS sighs loudly.)

PARIS: *Sigh*

JACKIE: Are you okay?

PARIS: Who me? Oh, I'm fine. *(PARIS sighs again, more loudly)* *SIGH*

JACKIE: You sure you're alright?

PARIS: Well, since you asked twice, I suppose I can reveal - It's just - well - I - I've lost my spark.

KEATON: Your spark?

PARIS: My creative spark, yes. You see, I used to be an artist, a divine artist. Actually, I was a savant. Every breath I took was a symphony, every step a ballet. I used to sneeze and a poem would come out. But now... nothing.

JACKIE: Well maybe if you -

PARIS: I try to string a sentence together and all that's left is silence.

KEATON: What if you - ?

PARIS: I try to come up with a dance and my limbs hardly move.

25

(PARIS raises their arms elegantly and does a lovely spin.)

KEATON: Actually, I think that looked sort of -

PARIS: It's like my soul was sucked out from my body, and now, I am naught but a hollow shell.

KEATON: Well, we're sorry to hear that, but we have a scene to write. So, if you don't mind -

PARIS: You're playwrights?

JACKIE: We are.

PARIS: Oh! I see! Not only have I lost my own spark, but now, I am a deterrent to your fine creative process. How devastating! *(PARIS collapses onto the floor.)* My body has given out! I am doomed to stay in this very place until my spark returns, which, in all likelihood, will never occur!

KEATON: Could you -?

PARIS: WHY ME!? Come back, little spark! Come back.

(PARIS sobs loudly.)

JACKIE: Wait. I have an idea.

(KEATON and JACKIE huddle together and whisper.)

PARIS: Of course you have an idea! You're full of ideas! And I have none! *(KEATON and JACKIE come to an agreement, and JACKIE starts writing again.)* What's that? You're writing? Ah yes, don't let me hinder your process. Just go on ignoring me. Ignore me as if I were nothing but thin air. Ignore me, as if I were a little speck of invisible dust, as if I - *(PARIS looks at their notebook.)* Wait a minute! - you're writing down everything I say.

(JACKIE scribbles furiously.)

JACKIE: We are.

(JACKIE writes again.)

PARIS: And you're writing down everything *you* say!

KEATON: It's a scene.

PARIS: I am a... a muse?

KEATON: And a playwright.

PARIS: Me? Little old me?

(JACKIE transcribes their conversation.)

JACKIE: "Me? Little old me?"

PARIS: Why, look at that! I'm a playwright. I'm brilliant! My spark! It's alive!

JACKIE: Congrats.

PARIS: Wow. I can't wait to see what I do next! I'd better go spread my gift! Farewell, friends! Farewell! How marvelous!

(PARIS exits dramatically.)

KEATON: So, where were we?

(JACKIE shrugs.)

- END SCENE -

CAMPING
(3 Actors)

(SAMMI, TERRY, and MEL are camping. SAMMI pitches a tent, while TERRY and MEL sit on the ground, looking up at the sky. Throughout the scene, SAMMI works tirelessly, while TERRY and MEL recline lazily. SAMMI is constantly in motion, setting up the campsite and making sure everything runs smoothly.)

TERRY: Ah, the great outdoors. Don't you love the smell of fresh air?

MEL: This is what it's all about: Truly being one with nature. Getting our hands dirty. Doing the hard work to survive.

SAMMI: Does the tent look kind of lopsided?

(MEL and TERRY look over at the tent.)

TERRY: Sort of.

MEL: Yeah.

(MEL and TERRY resume their conversation without getting up to help. SAMMI continues pitching the tent alone.)

TERRY: It feels so good to dedicate the time to disconnect and really test yourself.

MEL: Right? I mean, how great is it to actually build your own shelter?

(SAMMI grunts with strained effort. TERRY sighs contentedly.)

TERRY: Makes me feel strong.

MEL: Makes me feel capable.

(SAMMI finally fixes the tent and examines it happily.)

SAMMI: Fixed it! Tent's all set!

> *(SAMMI starts building a fire. MEL and TERRY stretch out and watch.)*

MEL: And making fire from nothing but a little wood and flint?

TERRY: Challenging.

MEL: Challenging, but meaningful.

> *(SAMMI rubs sticks together.)*

SAMMI: It's sparking!

> *(SAMMI blows at the base of the fire as it ignites. TERRY and MEL observe from a safe distance.)*

TERRY: It's like lighting the flame of our independence.

MEL: Woah. Yes.

SAMMI: It's lit! We have fire! I'll grab some more wood!

> *(SAMMI runs around collecting wood. MEL and TERRY watch the fire.)*

TERRY: People are so obsessed with their fancy heat, and air conditioning, and refrigerators.

MEL: Who needs it? We can fend for ourselves.

SAMMI: Here you go! More logs! *(SAMMI drops more logs on the fire, then pulls some trail mix out of their pocket.)* Trail mix, anyone?

MEL: Yes please.

TERRY: Yum!

> *(SAMMI gives MEL and TERRY some trail mix.)*

SAMMI: It's getting late. Wanna go down to the lake to catch some fish before the sun sets?

TERRY: Oh, that's okay. I can stay here and watch the fire.

MEL: Me too. You go, enjoy.

SAMMI: All right! I'll be back!

(*SAMMI exits cheerfully.*)

MEL: This is hard work.

TERRY: Exhausting. But worth it.

MEL: Totally.

- END SCENE -

DENTIST
(3 Actors)

(Note: Pronouns can be changed depending on whether ADRIAN is played by a boy or a girl.)

(Two siblings, COURTNEY and TRACI, sit in the waiting room at the dentist's office. TRACI looks petrified. COURTNEY comforts TRACI.)

TRACI: I don't floss. They told me to floss. And I told Mom I floss. But I don't floss. I really should floss.

COURTNEY: It's okay, Dr. Needleman is super nice. You don't need to be nervous.

> *(ADRIAN enters. ADRIAN has gauze in their mouth and is unable to speak properly. All of their text is unspoken. They communicate with muffled speech and large gestures, like charades. COURTNEY greets ADRIAN.)*

COURTNEY: Hi.

ADRIAN: [Hi there!]

TRACI: Wow. Hey, are you okay?

ADRIAN: [I'm great!]

TRACI: You can't talk? What did they do to you in there!?

ADRIAN: [They just pulled some baby teeth. I got some novocaine. It didn't hurt at all.]

TRACI: Courtney, she can't even talk! We're doomed!

ADRIAN: [No! Don't worry. This dentist is the best!]

COURTNEY: She doesn't look upset. You're not upset are you?

ADRIAN: [Not at all! I feel awesome!]

31

TRACI: Where's mom? I wanna get out of here!

COURTNEY: Hey, hey. Calm down. Mom's putting money in the meter. *(COURTNEY turns to ADRIAN.)* They're nice, right?

ADRIAN: [They're incredible. I love them.]

COURTNEY: Did you get teeth pulled?

ADRIAN: [Yes! Two molars.]

COURTNEY: And it wasn't so bad?

ADRIAN: [It was fine!]

COURTNEY: See, Traci? It was fine! *(COURTNEY turns back to ADRIAN.)* ... At least, I think that's what you said?

(ADRIAN nods happily.)

TRACI: I don't want to go in.

COURTNEY: Hey. Hey. It's okay. Listen, I used to be scared of the dentist too.

TRACI: Really?

(COURTNEY nods.)

COURTNEY: I used to feel sort of trapped. I'd cry, and then I was so embarrassed, I'd try to force myself to stop, which only made it worse. But this one time, I had a really nice hygienist. She said that *I* was in charge. She said we could stop whenever I said so and I could cry if I needed to, and then suddenly... I didn't need to anymore.

TRACI: Wow.

ADRIAN: [Double wow.]

COURTNEY: It's okay to feel a little anxious. You can even tell them you're scared. And if you want them to stop, just tell them you need a break.

32

TRACI: That's okay?

COURTNEY: Totally. Look, you don't have to go in if you don't want to, but I promise you, they just want to help you.

ADRIAN: [I used to be scared of dogs, but now I love them! I like little ones, and big ones, and fluffy ones, and not so fluffy ones.]

COURTNEY: Sorry, what did you say?

ADRIAN: [The dentist is just like the dogs!]

COURTNEY: Huh?

(They hear a voice calling from off-stage)

TRACI: I think they're calling my name.

COURTNEY: Want me to go first?

TRACI: No. I think I'm ready, actually.

COURTNEY: I can sit with you until Mom gets back if you want.

TRACI: That'd be nice. Thanks, Courtney. *(TRACI turns to ADRIAN.)* And thank you too. I feel much better now. Good luck with your mouth.

ADRIAN: [Thanks! I'm gonna go home and eat a lot of ice cream and watch movies with my dog, Patsy! I really really love dogs!]

TRACI: I love dogs too!

ADRIAN: [Right!?]

COURTNEY: You understood that?

TRACI: You didn't? C'mon we gotta get back there!

(TRACI waves goodbye to ADRIAN and heads back towards the dentist's office. COURTNEY follows.)

- END SCENE -

BASEBALL
(3 Actors)

(Note: Pronouns can be changed depending on whether JAMIE is played by a boy or a girl)

(JAMIE and LANE are on the sidelines at their baseball game. They're both waiting for their chance to step up to the plate. LANE practices their swing. JAMIE watches the game happily. Their teammate REESE enters.)

JAMIE: That was amazing!

(JAMIE high fives REESE.)

REESE: Thanks! Did you see how fast the ball was moving?

JAMIE: So fast! That was an amazing at bat.

LANE: But... didn't you just strike out?

JAMIE: Struck out with style!

LANE: Then why are you high-fiving? Striking out isn't the goal. You know that right?

JAMIE: Rosen is the best pitcher in the league.

REESE: She could go pro. And we get to hit against her!

LANE: You *want* her to strike you out?

JAMIE: It's an honor!

LANE: You can't be fans of your competition!

REESE: Why not?

JAMIE: I'm up! Wish me luck!

(JAMIE steps to the mound. We witness JAMIE's at bat, while REESE and LANE watch.)

35

LANE: She can't be *that* good at pitching.

REESE: You'll see.

(*JAMIE swings and misses.*)

LANE: Strike one!

REESE: Wow. The ball was moving so fast, it's hard to see!

LANE: I guess it was pretty fast. Like a blur.

(*JAMIE swings and misses again.*)

REESE: Strike two.

LANE: Woah! Was that a curveball?

REESE: Sure was! You got this, Jamie! Strike out with style!

(*Distracted, JAMIE looks over at LANE and REESE. In doing so, JAMIE steps onto the plate.*)

JAMIE: What'd you say?

LANE: Look out!

(*JAMIE gets hit by the ball and falls to the ground.*)

JAMIE: Ooof!

REESE: She's hit!

(*LANE and REESE rush over to JAMIE.*)

LANE: Oh no!

JAMIE: Oh wow. Oh wow. Oh wow.

LANE: Are you okay?

JAMIE (*ecstatic*): I just got hit by one of Rosen's pitches!!

REESE: Ah! That was amazing!

LANE: But are you hurt?

JAMIE (*happily*): Yes! It hurts so much!

REESE: I'm so jealous!!

JAMIE: Do you think she'll sign my bruise?

REESE: Maybe! She looks really sorry!

> (*JAMIE and REESE wave happily at Rosen off-stage and flash her thumbs up.*)
>
> (*JAMIE dusts off and gets up.*)

JAMIE: I can't believe it. I got a hit! I got a hit!

LANE: You got *hit.*

JAMIE: That's what I said!

REESE: Take your base! Take your base!

LANE: Shouldn't we stop the game?

JAMIE: Are you kidding!? First base, here I come! I can't wait to tell my grandkids!

> (*JAMIE limps off-stage to first base.*)
>
> *- END SCENE -*

SNOW DAY
(3 Actors)

(Three siblings in their bedroom. MURPHY and LANDRY look out the window, while DANI sits on a bed and reads.)

MURPHY: It's really coming down now.

LANDRY: C'mon, snow! Stick! Stiiiick!

MURPHY: I think it's getting heavier. What does the school website say? Anything?

(LANDRY looks at their phone.)

LANDRY: Nothing yet. *(LANDRY looks out the window again.)* I believe in you, little snowflakes! You can do it!

DANI: Can you two please be quiet? I'm trying to read.

LANDRY: How can you read when there may be a snow day!?

DANI: Staring out the window isn't going to make a difference.

MURPHY: You're right... We can't just *stand* here. We have to do some sort of snow day ritual.

LANDRY: Yes! That's genius.

DANI: Please tell me you're joking.

MURPHY: I did a snow day ceremony last year before that big storm, and school was canceled for two full days!

LANDRY: Ah! Amazing! Show me! Show me!

MURPHY: First we have to turn our sweatshirts inside out.

LANDRY: Yes!

(LANDRY and MURPHY turn their sweatshirts inside out.)

DANI: This is ridiculous.

MURPHY: Then we jump up and down six times.

(They jump.)

MURPHY & LANDRY: One, two, three, four, five, six!

MURPHY: Now we clap and chant: "More snow! Less school! More snow! Less school!"

(They clap their hands and chant, getting louder as they go. DANI covers his/her ears.)

MURPHY & LANDRY: "More snow! Less school! More snow! Less school! More snow! Less school! Woo!"

MURPHY: Refresh the school website!

(LANDRY looks at their phone.)

LANDRY: Okay! It says.... Ugh, still nothing. It didn't work!

MURPHY: I don't understand. It worked last time.

(DANI scoffs.)

LANDRY: Maybe it's because Dani didn't do it!

DANI: Or because snow rituals don't work.

MURPHY: C'mon, Dani! Please?

LANDRY: I need to have a day off to go sledding, and drink hot chocolate, and cuddle up under the covers, and be all COZY! Please please please! *(LANDRY falls to their knees.)* PLEASE!!!

DANI: Okay. Okay. Fine. I'll do it. Then I can read in peace.

MURPHY & LANDRY: Hooray!!

(DANI gets up and joins in.)

MURPHY: First, we jump!

> *(They all jump six times. DANI starts out reluctantly, but then picks up steam.)*

ALL: One, two, three, four, five, six!

> *(They clap their hands and chant, getting more and more excited as they go.)*

ALL: "More snow! Less school! More snow! Less school! More snow! Less school! Woo!"

MURPHY: Check the website! Check the website!

> *(LANDRY looks at their phone.)*

LANDRY: It says... Nothing. No updates.

MURPHY: I thought for sure that one would work. I guess you were right, Dani.

LANDRY: Sorry for interrupting your reading. We won't bother you anymore.

> *(LANDRY and MURPHY hang their heads and walk towards the exit.)*

DANI: Wait!

MURPHY: What?

DANI: My sweatshirt wasn't inside out!

LANDRY: Again! Again!

> *(DANI turns their sweatshirt inside out.)*

MURPHY: Ready?

DANI: Let's do it!

> *- END SCENE -*

SKIING
(3 Actors)

(BRETT, DYLAN, and CAMERON stand at the top of a small ski slope.)

BRETT: This is just the bunny slope, okay? Nothing to worry about.

DYLAN: Woo! Slope time!

CAMERON: Seems pretty high. Seems *really* high.

BRETT: Now, just like we discussed: move your skis into the shape of a pizza. *(CAMERON and DYLAN move their skis into a pizza shape.)* Good! We'll glide down the slope at an angle, and that pizza shape will help us go nice and slow.

(DYLAN spots some fast skiers and points them out.)

DYLAN: They aren't doing pizza.

BRETT: *They* aren't beginners. We'll work our way up to french fry.

DYLAN: Wow, they're fast! French fry looks awesome!

CAMERON: I'm good with slow. The slower the better. In fact, maybe I'll just stay up here for a while.

BRETT: C'mon, you're doing great. We're all gonna work our way down together. Ready? Nice and slow.

CAMERON: Okay...

(They all start skiing down the mountain slowly and methodically. CAMERON is terrified. DYLAN seems bored.)

ALL: Pizza.
Pizza.
Pizza.
Pizza.

41

BRETT: You're looking great!

ALL: Pizza.
   Pizza.

DYLAN: Forget this! I wanna french fry!!!!

> *(DYLAN turns their skis parallel to one another.)*

BRETT: Wait! Don't!

CAMERON: Careful!

> *(But it's too late, DYLAN is zooming down the mountain. At first, DYLAN is ecstatic, then fearful.)*

DYLAN: French fry!!
   French fry!!
   Oh no french fry!!
   French fry?!
   Ahhhh freeeenncchh fryyyy!!

> *(DYLAN zooms off-stage.)*

BRETT: Hold on, I'm coming!

> *(BRETT zooms off after DYLAN, leaving CAMERON alone on stage, frozen in place.)*

CAMERON: Umm.... hello? Anyone? *(CAMERON takes a deep breath.)* You got this. You can do it. *(CAMERON skis down the mountain, gaining confidence and speed over time.)*
   Pizza.
   Pizza.
   Pizza!
   Pizza!!
   Pizza!!!
   PIZZA!!!
   (CAMERON arrives at the bottom of the mountain.)
   Woo! I made it.
   Anyone else *really* craving a slice of pizza?

> *- END SCENE -*

PIGEONS
(5 Actors)

(Five pigeons in a park. They bob their heads back and forth as pigeons do and prance through the park, flapping their wings.)

BUDDY: Ladies, Gentlemen. It's wonderful to see you.

KIWI: Indeed! You're looking quite dapper today.

PEPPER: Beautiful feathers. Pristine.

BUDDY: Why thank you. I bathed in puddle water just this morning.

TANGO: Ah, and which puddle water did you select?

BUDDY: Only the best.

ORVILLE: Ah?

BUDDY: Muddy puddle water.

ALL: Wow.

ORVILLE: Very nice! It does show.

BUDDY: And you're looking particularly regal today, Orville. Is that... sewage I smell?

ORVILLE: Good nose, lad! The finest sewage from the New York subway system. I used it for my talon pedicure this morning.

TANGO: Marvelous!

PEPPER: The subway is a delightful spa. I visited once and exfoliated my beak with the steam coming up from the platform.

TANGO: How indulgent!

(KIWI spots something and shrinks away.)

KIWI: Oh no. Not again.

BUDDY: Whatever is the matter?

KIWI: Humans approaching.

> *(All of the pigeons scuttle away in fear. They watch the humans from afar.)*

ORVILLE: Filthy creatures.

BUDDY: The way they move.

TANGO: Awkward.

BUDDY: Their bodies.

KIWI: So lanky.

PEPPER: And they take up the entire street, as if they don't care that we're here!

BUDDY: Oh no, they're getting close!

TANGO: Stay away, humans!

ORVILLE: Too close! Too close! Let's go! Fly! Fly!

> *(The pigeons all take flight. Leaving the stage)*

> *(After a moment, KIWI re-enters, cautiously looking around.)*

KIWI: I think they're gone.

> *(The other pigeons return slowly.)*

ORVILLE: No self-awareness, those humans.

TANGO: None at all.

> *- END SCENE -*

LAUGHING CONTEST
(4 Actors)

(SAM and SYDNEY stomp into the school parking lot and come face to face with MAX and MARTI. They all look menacing and deeply serious, like they're about to fight.)

MAX: So, you accepted my challenge.

SAM: 'Course I did. I'm no wimp.

(MAX gestures to SYDNEY)

MAX: Is that your second?

SAM: Yup. *(SAM gestures to MARTI)* That yours?

MAX: Sure is.

MARTI: You ready to rumble?

SYDNEY: I was *born* ready.

MARTI: Let's do it then.

(MAX and MARTI face off against SAM and SYDNEY. After a tense silence, SAM begins.)

SAM: Ha.

MAX: HA.

SYDNEY: HA HA.

MARTI: HA HA HA!

(As they laugh, their gestures get more and more inventive, wild, and energetic.)

SAM: Tee hee.

MAX: Tee hee hee hee.

45

SYDNEY: Ho ho ha ha HA!

MARTI: Muahahahaha!

SYDNEY & SAM: ha ha ha ha ha ha ha ha ha!

MARTI & MAX: HAHAHAHAHAHAHAHA!

SYDNEY & SAM: AHHHH HAHAHAHAHAHAHAHA!

MARTI & MAX: BAHAHAHAHAHAHAHA!

SYNDEY & SAM: HAHAHAHAHHAHAHAHAHAHA!

MARTI & MAX: HAHAHAHAHAHAHA!

SYNDEY & SAM & MARTI & MAX:
HAHAHAHAHHAHAHAHAHAHA!

> *(The four competitors devolve into a fit of laughter. They roll around on the floor giggling and laughing hysterically.)*
>
> *(Eventually, their laughter subsides and they stand up and face one another. Once all of the giggles are gone, they become remarkably serious once more.)*

MAX: Truce?

SAM: Truce.

> *(They shake hands.)*
>
> *- END SCENE -*

THE PITCH
(3 Actors)

(RUDY, SAM, and MASON stand in the doorway of their neighbor's house. They face downstage and look out at the audience, addressing their off-stage neighbor who we don't see.)

RUDY: Excuse me ma'am, sorry to bother you.

MASON: We don't wanna take up too much of your time.

SAM: You seem extremely busy, am I right?

(Their off-stage neighbor agrees.)

MASON: We thought so.

RUDY: We know you have a lot on your plate. Life can be chaotic, stressful, and downright ugly.

SAM: Though *you* look great!

MASON: Really fabulous.

(Their off-stage neighbor grows impatient and tries to shoo them away.)

SAM: Okay, okay. Sorry, we'll get to the point.

RUDY: We're your friendly neighborhood chore team.

SAM: We're here to do the chores you don't wanna do!

MASON: Need someone to help you out? That's us!

ALL: We work hard for *you!*

RUDY: At very affordable rates.

(Their off-stage neighbor grows interested and lists some chores she needs help with. First, she mentions mowing the lawn.)

SAM: Well no, we don't have a lawn mower, so we don't really do that...

(She mentions washing the car.)

MASON: Washing the car? Oh. Well, that seems like a big responsibility...

(She mentions cleaning some dishes.)

RUDY: Dishes? Ooo I have delicate hands so... no, not that either.

(Their off-stage neighbor gets frustrated and asks them what exactly they WOULD help with.)

SAM: Now that you ask, I guess I hadn't thought about it too much.

MASON: Me either.

RUDY: Oh! If you have any leftover food you want eaten, we could do that.

MASON: Yeah! Or if you want someone to play with your dog.

SAM: Though we don't want to pick up any.... *you know.*

MASON: We could watch some shows to make sure your premium channels are working!

(The neighbor says no.)

SAM: Well, all right. Maybe next time?

RUDY: Okay. Thanks anyway.

MASON: Bye now.

(The neighbor closes the door. MASON, SAM, and RUDY turn to one another.)

MASON: Tough sell, huh?

SAM: Yeah, what's her deal?

RUDY: Let's go next door. Maybe they need help trying out those new bikes they got for Christmas.

MASON: For a reasonable price.

RUDY: Of course.

    - END SCENE -

NURSE'S OFFICE
(4 Actors)

(Note: Pronouns can be changed depending on whether ALEX is played by a boy or a girl.)

(ALEX, CRIS, and DYLAN are in the nurse's office. The nurse just left the room.)

ALEX *(To CRIS)*: What're you in for?

CRIS: Excuse me?

ALEX: What're you in for? Stomachache? Headache? Toothache? Toe-ache?

DYLAN: You don't have to answer that.

ALEX: Of course you don't *have* to answer it, but how else are we gonna pass the time in here? These books are seriously old. I've already read this one like twelve times.

CRIS: You spend a lot of time in the nurse's office, huh?

ALEX: Oh yeah.

DYLAN: Alex is a regular.

CRIS: You must be really sick.

ALEX: I suffer from a very serious disease called hypochondria.

CRIS: Hypo- huh?

DYLAN: Means she's scared of getting sick. Whatever you do, don't tell her any of your symptoms or she'll think she has them too. I have asthma, so I'm here every so often, and I always see...

(ALEX starts hyperventilating.)

ALEX: Can't. Breathe.

DYLAN: Oh, quit it! You don't have asthma.

ALEX: Right. Sorry.

DYLAN: What brings you in today, Alex?

ALEX: Well, during second period, Molly Markowitz told me about her rash, and I just started itching all over. It was unbearable, like my skin was crawling with little insects! I was about to give my final presentation in Mr. Collin's class, but he sent me to the nurse instead.

DYLAN: I was gonna give my presentation during first period, but then my symptoms acted up!

CRIS: I was supposed to be in his class third period! But then I got a stomachache...

ALEX: Ugh! My stomach! It hurts!

CRIS: ...But it feels a lot better now.

ALEX: Hey, mine does too!

DYLAN: I feel pretty good now also.

(BLAKE enters.)

BLAKE: Oh wow, it's crowded in here.

DYLAN: There's a bed over there. The nurse will be back soon.

BLAKE: Thanks!

ALEX: So what you got?

DYLAN: You don't have to answer that.

BLAKE: Me? Oh well... I have a lot of things... a lot. Let me see here... I have, um, planter warts and wobbly ankles, I got shin splints, and I think I need a knee replacement. *(ALEX mimics all of the symptoms as BLAKE lists them.)* My hamstrings are really tight, and my hips... don't even ask. I think my kidneys are failing and my liver's a mess. My lungs aren't working right, and my heart's beating super fast. I have digestive issues. My arms are wonky and my hands are jittery. My armpits smell really bad. My neck is stiff. My head is all stuffed up.

ALEX: I don't feel so hot!

(DYLAN comforts ALEX.)

DYLAN: It's okay, Alex. You're okay.

CRIS *(to BLAKE)*: That's terrible. How long has this been going on?

BLAKE: Well, I was feeling fine this morning, but then, I was walking over to -

CRIS, DYLAN, & ALEX *(interrupting)*: Mr. Collin's class!!?

BLAKE: How'd you know?!

CRIS: Final presentations, right?

(BLAKE nods.)

DYLAN: Same here.

ALEX: Me too.

BLAKE: Really?

(They all nod.)

CRIS: If it helps, I think you're a pretty great public speaker.

DYLAN: Yeah, you're awesome.

ALEX: Very impressive.

BLAKE: Wow. Thanks!

- END SCENE -

PASSING NOTES
(3 Actors)

(Note: pronouns can be changed depending on whether SPENCER and VAL are played by a boy or girl).

(SPENCER, TATUM, and VAL sit in a row in class. SPENCER writes a note and passes it to TATUM, whispering.)

SPENCER: Psst! Can you pass this to Val?

TATUM: I'm trying to focus.

SPENCER: Please?

TATUM: Fine.

(TATUM turns to VAL.)

TATUM: This is from Spencer.

VAL: No thanks.

TATUM: Just take it.

VAL: I'm not talking to Spencer.

TATUM: What? Why not?

VAL: He knows why.

TATUM: Okay...*(TATUM turns to SPENCER.)* Here. Take it back. Val doesn't want it.

SPENCER: What!? Why not?

TATUM: You know why.

SPENCER: Clearly I don't.

(SPENCER scribbles something else on the piece of paper.)

SPENCER: Can you give this to Val?

TATUM: Why don't you just talk after class?

SPENCER: I can't stand it when people are mad at me. I need to know what's going on or I'm gonna lose it!

TATUM: Ugh. Fine. *(TATUM turns to VAL.)* This is from Spencer. He doesn't know why you're mad.

VAL: Well he should!

TATUM: Can't you just take it so I can get back to paying attention?

VAL: Fine.

> *(VAL takes the note, looks directly at SPENCER, crumples the note in a ball and throws it on the ground. SPENCER is horrified. TATUM is exasperated. SPENCER takes out another piece of paper and starts scribbling ferociously.)*

TATUM *(to SPENCER)*: Don't even think about passing that to me.

SPENCER: You tell Val - you say - ugh - tell Val, now *I'm* not talking to *her*!

TATUM: Great. How about we all just stop talking since we're in the middle of a lesson and we have a test tomorrow?

> *(SPENCER leans over TATUM and speaks directly to VAL in a whisper.)*

SPENCER: Now *I'm* not talking to *you*.

VAL: Good.

> *(Silence falls.)*

TATUM: Finally.

> *(SPENCER and VAL break out into fast, aggressive whispers again.)*

SPENCER *(to VAL):* Why are you mad at me!?

VAL: As if you didn't deliberately exclude me!

SPENCER: Exclude you from what?!

TATUM: Keep your voices down.

VAL: Aren't you having a birthday party on Saturday?

SPENCER: Yes.

VAL: And where, exactly, was my invite?

SPENCER: I sent it last month! My note was asking you why you didn't RSVP!

VAL: Really?

SPENCER: Really.

VAL: Oh. *(Beat.)* I'd love to come.

SPENCER: Great. I'll be sure to get a vanilla cake since that's your favorite.

VAL: Great.

SPENCER: Then that's that.

VAL: That's that.

> *(Beat.)*

> *(SPENCER leans over to TATUM and whispers.)*

SPENCER: Phew. Thanks. I'm glad nobody's mad at me.

TATUM *(angrily):* You're having a birthday party on Saturday?

SPENCER: Um.

- END SCENE -

OVERHEARD
(3 Actors)

[PLEASE NOTE: This scene deals with sensitive issues. Please use your judgement to determine whether or not it's appropriate for your young performers.]

(Two siblings – CAMERON and MORGAN – press their ears up to a heating vent, listening to their parents argue downstairs. Their third sibling, SKYLER, enters.)

SKYLER: What are you two doing?

CAMERON: Shhh... We're listening.

MORGAN: Mom and Dad are fighting.

SKYLER: Again? *(MORGAN nods. SKYLER joins their siblings at the vent. They all listen intently.)* What're they saying?

CAMERON: I can't make it out, but they seem mad.

MORGAN: Dad's using his super stern low voice and Mom keeps yelling.

SYKLER: Mom never yells. Or I guess, she never *used to* yell. Now she yells.

MORGAN: I asked her about it last week.

CAMERON: You did? What'd she say?

MORGAN: She said everything was fine and I shouldn't worry about it.

SKYLER: It doesn't sound fine.

CAMERON: Sh! It got quiet.

SKYLER *(whispering)*: Do you think they made up?

MORGAN: I hope so!

CAMERON: Oh no. Was that the front door?

MORGAN: Is someone leaving?

SKYLER: Quick. To the window!

(They all rush over to the window and look outside.)

CAMERON: Dad.

MORGAN: Where's he going?

SKYLER: He'll be back soon, right?

MORGAN: I don't know.

SKYLER: This is bad. Really bad.

(CAMERON takes a deep breath.)

CAMERON: It's okay. We'll be okay.

(They hear their mother crying off-stage.)

MORGAN: Oh no. Is Mom crying?

SKYLER: Mom never cries.

(MORGAN and SKYLER move back towards the vent to listen.)

CAMERON: Wait. Don't listen any more. Just - just come back.

(MORGAN and SKYLER move away from the vent.)

SKYLER: I'm worried.

CAMERON: I know.

MORGAN: He left.

CAMERON: I know. Come here. *(CAMERON hugs their siblings.)* Let's just stay right here for a minute.

(They hug.)

- END SCENE -

CHEERS!
(3 Actors)

(Three siblings – JAN, HUDSON, and BAILEY – stand in front of their family at their grandmother's 80th birthday party. They face the audience downstage, speaking to their off-stage family who we don't see. They raise their glasses.)

JAN: We'd like to propose a toast to Nana.

HUDSON: Happy 80th birthday, Nana!

BAILEY: You don't look a day over 95.

(The off-stage family doesn't react well to this, except for Nana who laughs uproariously.)

JAN: That was a joke. It was supposed to be funny. Why is Nana the only one laughing?

(BAILEY taps her microphone.)

BAILEY: Is this thing on?

HUDSON *(to JAN)*: Quick. Next joke. Next joke.

JAN: Anyway... We, uh, really admire you for working so hard and raising a great family.

BAILEY: You are the best mother and grandmother around.

HUDSON: Though maybe you could have done a better job with Dad, am I right?

(Their off-stage Dad gets up and angrily storms out of the party. The kids react.)

JAN: Aw, Dad! We're just joking around. Don't leave!

(Their off-stage mom shoots them a scathing look and follows their dad.)

HUDSON: Mom! Come back!

BAILEY: At least Nana got it. Look at her cracking up.

JAN *(to HUDSON)*: Don't stop. Keep going.

HUDSON: So, um, we're really glad to be your grandkids.

BAILEY: You give great advice.

JAN: And, more importantly, you give *really* expensive birthday presents.

> *(The off-stage family is angry. Nana is the only one who laughs. Several family members leave.)*

BAILEY: Wait! Don't go!

JAN: Uncle Joe! Get back here.

HUDSON: Come on, Aunt Betty, I sat through two of your daughter's piano recitals and she's no Mozart! *(The rest of the family is livid. They all get up to leave. Only Nana remains.)* Wait! I didn't mean that! You're very talented, Cindy. I love "Chopsticks"!

BAILEY: Please stay! You can't all go!

HUDSON: You're going to leave Nana here alone on her birthday?!

JAN: Wow. Tough crowd.

> *(The kids look out at their only remaining family member.)*

BAILEY: Thanks for sticking it out, Nana.

JAN: Should we finish?

> *(Nana nods off-stage.)*

BAILEY: To put it simply: Nana, we think you may be our favorite person in the whole entire world.

JAN: Thanks for getting us and for supporting us.

HUDSON: We love you a lot.

JAN: And that's no joke.

BAILEY: Here's to Nana!

ALL: To Nana!

- END SCENE -

TALENT SHOW
(5 Actors)

(RILEY, BRETT, DREW, QUINN, and CAMERON are on stage at the school talent show. They speak to the audience.)

RILEY: Ladies and Gentleman, welcome to the talent show! Thank you for coming.

QUINN: We're going to do a dance for you.

BRETT: Which we choreographed ourselves.

DREW: We spent lots of time preparing.

CAMERON: And we definitely didn't get distracted playing video games during our rehearsals.*(They all shoot CAMERON an annoyed look.)* What?

(RILEY looks off-stage.)

RILEY: Ms. Conrow, can you turn on the music? Thank you.

(The music starts. The five performers begin to dance. It's clear they have not rehearsed properly. RILEY is the only one who remembers the dance. DREW, BRETT, and QUINN all trip over one another, trying to keep up. CAMERON dances to the beat of their own drum, ignoring the choreography entirely.)

DREW: Whoops.

BRETT: Ouch!

QUINN: Sorry.

DREW: What comes next?

(RILEY moves to the front and tries to lead them, whispering to the group.)

RILEY: Just follow me. I know it.

(RILEY does some impressive moves, but the others are unable to imitate them. They frantically try to follow.)

BRETT: Too fast! I can't keep up!

DREW: Smile, everyone. Smile and they won't notice.

QUINN *(to RILEY)*: Nobody can follow you. Slow down.

RILEY: Sorry. Is this better?

(RILEY slows down a lot, moving really really slowly.)

BRETT: Too slow! Too slow!

QUINN *(to RILEY)*: Pick up the pace!

(RILEY dances a bit faster. BRETT, DREW, and QUINN try to mirror RILEY. CAMERON is oblivious.)

BRETT: This is a disaster!

DREW: Keep dancing everyone. Just keep dancing.

(CAMERON dances and waves to the audience.)

CAMERON: Hi Mom! Hey Steve! Lookin' sharp!

RILEY: We're off the beat!

BRETT: There's a beat?

RILEY: We shouldn't have played all those video games.

(QUINN starts to feel nauseous.)

QUINN: Uh oh. I think I - I feel - I gotta - !

(Sick, QUINN covers their mouth and rushes off stage.)

BRETT: Oh no. You okay?

(BRETT rushes off after QUINN. DREW and RILEY exchange worried looks. CAMERON doesn't notice.)

RILEY: What do we do?

DREW: We're almost done. We can do this. Keep going.

CAMERON: This is a great song.

(RILEY spots their dad in the audience.)

RILEY: Oh my goodness. Is my dad filming this? Ugh! I can't take it!

(Mortified, RILEY rushes off stage.)

DREW: Wait! You're the only one who knows the moves! Come back!

(DREW runs after RILEY.)

(CAMERON, alone, looks out at the audience and grins.)

CAMERON: Hey everyone! Watch this!! *(CAMERON does some exuberant, goofy dance moves.)* Thank you.

(CAMERON bows.)

- END SCENE -

THE CANDY
(4 Actors)

(Summer camp. FINN and MO stand outside the cafeteria and watch it intently.)

FINN: Any second now, she'll leave and we can sneak in the side door.

(PERRY and JAY walk by and overhear their conversation.)

MO: I can't wait to get in there!

PERRY: Get in where?

(Startled, FINN and MO jump.)

MO: Ah!

FINN: You shouldn't sneak up on people!

JAY: Sorry.

FINN: Why aren't you two down by the lake?

PERRY: We already passed our swim tests.

JAY: We got a permission slip to go back to the bunk. Did you get one too?

(JAY holds up the permission slip. FINN and MO look at each other nervously.)

FINN: Um...

PERRY: You're not allowed to be here, are you?

FINN: Keep your voice down!

PERRY: Tell us what you're up to!

MO: We're breaking into the cafeteria! There's piles of Butterfingers and mounds of Mounds Bars in there! We take them when nobody's watching!

FINN: Mo! Don't tell them that!

MO: Whoops! Sorry. I'm just so excited!... And nervous!

PERRY: That's amazing! I'd do anything for Butterfingers. Can we come?

JAY: What?

PERRY: We'll help you carry the candy. We're really strong.

FINN: Well... alright. So long as you do as I say.

PERRY: Deal.

JAY: What about the counselors?

FINN: They're still at the lake. We're all alone. It's the perfect time to make our move.

JAY: But... um, isn't that sort of like... stealing?

FINN: Oh pah-lease. They stole all my candy on the first day of camp. They raided our bunk.

MO: It's true. They went through all my stuff. Even my pillowcase.

PERRY: Why would they look in your pillowcase?

MO: They saw crumbs.

PERRY: Huh?

MO: That's where I keep my Oreos!

FINN: Oh look! She's putting on her shoes! I think she's leaving!

MO: She's leaving! She's leaving! Look at her go!

PERRY: The coast is clear!

FINN: Quick! Before anyone sees!

(They move towards the exit. JAY blocks them.)

JAY: Wait! What if we get caught?

PERRY: We won't get caught. The cafeteria is empty. Look!

JAY: I'm sorry I - We shouldn't.

PERRY: This is what camp is for. We're just having fun.

FINN: Yeah, lighten up. You always ruin the fun.

JAY: I'm sorry. I - I didn't mean to...

FINN: We're going. *(FINN and PERRY move towards the exit. MO stays behind.)* Come on, Mo.

MO: I'll hang back.

PERRY: The Butterfingers are waiting!

FINN: We're not gonna bring any back for you, you know? We can't carry it all.

MO: That's fine. I'm good.

FINN: Ugh, whatever.

(PERRY and FINN exit.)

JAY: You didn't have to do that.

MO: Camp's supposed to be fun, right?

JAY: Yeah.

(MO shrugs.)

MO: I think you're fun.

- END SCENE -

MOVIE NIGHT
(4 Actors)

(CHARLIE, HOLLIS, JO, and SKYLAR sit on the couch, watching a scary movie. They're all terrified, but trying to play it cool.)

CHARLIE: I'm so glad we're watching this movie.

JO: Yeah. Me too.

CHARLIE: I know some people think it's scary, but I think it's great.

SKYLAR: Totally. I'm not scared at all.

HOLLIS: It's more funny than scary really.

CHARLIE: Totally!

(Something scary happens in the movie, and they all yell in fear.)

ALL: Ahh!

HOLLIS: That was ...hilarious.

SKYLAR: So funny. Almost too funny. That's why I didn't laugh.

CHARLIE: Let's definitely watch the whole movie. Let's definitely not *stop* watching, right?

SKYLAR: Yeah. Yeah. No reason to stop.

JO: Unless one of us was afraid? Then we would stop.

SKYLAR: Well, I'm not afraid.

HOLLIS: Me neither.

CHARLIE: I think this is my new favorite movie of all time.

(Something shocking happens in the movie, and they all gasp.)

HOLLIS: That looked painful.

JO: But cool.

CHARLIE: So cool.

SKYLAR: I can't wait to see what happens next.

CHARLIE: Me either! ...Though, um, it's a little hard to see right?

SKYLAR: What do you mean?

CHARLIE: There's a glare on the screen. It must be the sun coming through the window. If it's bothering any of you, we could maybe, um, do something else?

HOLLIS: From the sun? It's dark out.

SKYLAR *(to the screen)*: Don't go in there!

> *(Something gross happens in the movie and SKYLAR covers their eyes. Everyone winces.)*

JO: Yeah! A glare! I see it too. It's right there!

CHARLIE: Makes it hard to focus on this *awesome* movie, right?

JO: Yes! I am *loving* this movie, but the glare is in the way! Maybe we should turn off the tv?

HOLLIS: Glare? I don't see any glare? Where is it?

SKYLAR: Oh! I see it! I see it! It's a very annoying, very large, sort of, um, *blue* glare.

HOLLIS: Blue? That doesn't make any sense.

CHARLIE: It's a glaring glare, which will make us *turn off* the movie...

HOLLIS: Ohhhh! A *glare*! Yes! It's totally there! Amazing! I mean... how terrible.

JO: I'll turn it off right now.

(JO gets up and turns off the tv.)

HOLLIS: I guess we'll have to do something else.

CHARLIE: What a shame.

JO: Total bummer.

SKYLAR: If only there weren't a glare.

- END SCENE -

AMUSEMENT PARK
(5 Actors)

(TAYLOR, DAKOTA, AIDEN, CAMERON, and EMERSON wait in line for a roller coaster at an amusement park.)

TAYLOR: This is the longest line in the history of all lines! I'm so BORED.

(They move forward in the line.)

DAKOTA: We're almost there! We're about to turn the corner!

(AIDEN stares at their watch nervously.)

AIDEN: We have to meet up with the chaperones in 15 minutes on the other side of the park. Correction: 14 minutes!

DAKOTA: We'll make it! Don't worry. The rollercoaster only lasts like three minutes tops.

TAYLOR: I can't believe we've been waiting for almost an hour for a three-minute ride!

CAMERON: I hope it doesn't go upside-down. I don't like it when they go upside-down.

EMERSON: Wow that breeze feels good. And it's sunny! It's nice to be outside.

TAYLOR: How much longer?

DAKOTA: Any second now. See? We're turning the corner! It's happening.

(They move forward in the line again, turning a new direction.)

AIDEN: Oh no.

(Their faces fall as they see another part of the line that was hidden before.)

TAYLOR: There's ANOTHER part of this line!?

AIDEN: Why would they hide part of the line behind a wall!? It's immoral!

DAKOTA: Don't panic! We still have time.

AIDEN: 13 minutes! We're going to be late!

DAKOTA: We're so close!

TAYLOR: I can't keep standing here! I'll evaporate from boredom!

EMERSON: It's not so bad. We're together, right?

CAMERON: Are there seatbelts on this ride? Can you see? I can't see.

TAYLOR: This is agony!

EMERSON: Let's play a game!

AIDEN: A game? But we're in line.

TAYLOR: The line that never ends!

CAMERON: Do you think anyone has ever fallen off before?

EMERSON: C'mon! Let's play a game. Okay? I spy ... something beautiful!

TAYLOR: There isn't anything beautiful. We're in line!

AIDEN: 12 and a half minutes!

CAMERON: I spy seatbelts! See!? Seatbelts are beautiful, right?

EMERSON: Sure are! What else?

DAKOTA: I spy the line moving! That's good.

(They move forward.)

73

TAYLOR: I spy a cute baby! Over there. Look.

(They look.)

ALL: Awwww!

AIDEN: I spy popcorn. Smells pretty good.

EMERSON: Nice! But not what I was looking at. Any other
guesses?

DAKOTA: The clouds?

AIDEN: Taylor's sneakers?

TAYLOR: Aw, you like 'em? Thanks!

CAMERON: That juggler?

*(They all look. None of them had noticed the juggler
before.)*

DAKOTA: Woah! Cool!

EMERSON: Nope!

CAMERON: I guess there *are* cool things around here.

TAYLOR: That cafe with the pretty awning?

DAKOTA: That mural?

(They arrive at the front of the line.)

AIDEN: The - wow! We made it. With minutes to spare.

DAKOTA: We what? - Oh! We made it!!

CAMERON: These are really nice seatbelts!

DAKOTA: We did it! C'mon let's get on!

TAYLOR: Aww.

EMERSON: What's wrong?

TAYLOR: I kinda wish we could stay in line.

- END SCENE -

ZOO
(6 Actors)

(Three kids, HARPER, KEEGAN, and CARMEN, are on a field trip at the zoo. HARPER spots the monkey exhibit.)

HARPER: Monkeys look! Over there!

CARMEN: This zoo has monkeys?

(They run up to the cage and stare at the MONKEYS inside.)

KEEGAN: Aww wow! Look at 'em!

(Three monkeys, BOBO, TOOTSIE, and CHEEKS, stare back at the kids.)

BOBO: More children.

TOOTSIE: Don't they ever tire of staring at us?

CHEEKS: My, they look so foolish.

BOBO: Ridiculous.

(The kids make faces at the monkeys.)

HARPER: Look how funny they look.

KEEGAN: Check it out! Do I look like them?

(KEEGAN imitates the monkeys, making exaggerated monkey noises and motions.)

(The monkeys react.)

CHEEKS: Goodness, not again.

TOOTSIE: What are they doing?

BOBO: Human children are so absurd.

(CHEEKS imitates the human children.)

CHEEKS: How would one imitate such behavior? Do I look like them?

BOBO: Yes! Yes! You look exactly like them.

> *(All of the KIDS and the MONKEYS join in, imitating one another in large, exaggerated movements and sounds. They mirror one another, their movements growing more and more absurd over time. Finally, exhausted, they stop.)*

TOOTSIE: Human children are quite odd.

HARPER: Monkeys are really odd.

CHEEKS: I'd be so embarrassed if I were them.

KEEGAN: Talk about humiliating.

BOBO: Someone should teach them some manners.

CARMEN: Wow. I'm glad I'm not like that.

- END SCENE -

WEDDING
(4 Actors)

(PJ, SAGE, NICKI, and CASEY stand on the edge of the dance floor at a wedding.)

PJ: I've never seen something so terrifying.

NICKI: It's like they're possessed or something.

SAGE: They won't stop flailing.

(CASEY calls out to the people on the dance floor.)

CASEY: Stop flailing!

PJ: Can they hear the music?

SAGE: No rhythm. None at all.

CASEY: C'mon people! Listen to the beat!

NICKI: I thought my dad was the worst, but Aunt Cindy....

SAGE: Where's Aunt Cindy?

PJ: Over there.

SAGE: Oh. No no no no no. Someone make her stop.

CASEY: Aunt Cindy, what are you doing!?

NICKI: People over the age of 40 really shouldn't dance at weddings.

SAGE: There should be a law.

PJ: They have no shame.

SAGE: Should we pull them off the dance floor?

PJ: We tried earlier. They wouldn't come.

NICKI: They have no coordination, but they're pretty strong.

SAGE: We could try to get the band to stop playing. Maybe fake an emergency?

CASEY: I could pretend to pass out!

SAGE: Good idea!

CASEY: Okay!

> *(CASEY pretends to pass out. The other kids play along, exaggerating their reactions.)*

NICKY: Oh! No! It looks like Casey passed out!

PJ: Casey, are you okay?!

NICKI: What should we do?!

SAGE: Maybe everyone should stop dancing!

> *(They look around at the adults who are still dancing. CASEY pops their head up.)*

CASEY: Anything?

NICKI: They didn't even notice!

> *(CASEY yells at the band.)*

CASEY: Stop playing Earth Wind & Fire! You're making it worse!

PJ: Wait. What's going on over there? Why's everyone cheering?

NICKI: I can't see. They're all crowding around.

CASEY: Is that...?

SAGE: It can't be... !

NICKI: Nana!?

SAGE: Is she popping and locking!?

NICKI: Sure is!

PJ: She's INCREDIBLE!

NICKI: I've never seen anything like it.

ALL: Go Nana! Go Nana! Go Nana!

NICKI: Wow!

PJ: Let's go get a better look!

SAGE: C'mon!

CASEY: Nana, you're on fire!!

(They all exit, rushing towards the dance floor.)

- END SCENE -

HIKING
(4 Actors)

(AUGUST, KAI, and CLAY happily hike up a steep mountain. JAMIE lags behind, panting.)

AUGUST: This is great! Isn't this great?

CLAY: The absolute best. I love hiking. I could not be happier!

KAI: How're you doing back there, Jamie?

JAMIE *(panting heavily)*: I'm ... I'm... I... How?.... Who?... Why?

KAI: Wow, the air smells great.

AUGUST: So fresh and woodsy.

JAMIE *(wheezing)*: I can taste my heart beating.

KAI: We only have another little climb.

CLAY: Aww. Such a shame. This has been awesome.

AUGUST: We're just heading up that trail there. See?

JAMIE: This better be worth it.

CLAY: Oh trust us. It's incredible.

(They resume hiking. JAMIE climbs wearily on all fours while the others climb exuberantly.)

CLAY: Almost there.

AUGUST: Just a little bit more.

(They arrive at the peak.)

KAI: Ah! We made it!

(KAI, CLAY, and AUGUST happily soak in the view.)

CLAY: Amazing!

AUGUST: Wow. The lake looks so small from all the way up here.

KAI: Yeah. It really does.

(JAMIE looks around.)

JAMIE: ... um. Did I miss something...? This is it!? This is "made it"?

AUGUST: Well, yeah. Check out the view.

(They gesture to the stunning view.)

JAMIE: Where's the peak!?

AUGUST: This is the peak.

JAMIE: Where?

KAI: What do you mean? This is the top of the mountain: the peak.

JAMIE: I thought the peak was a restaurant. You said we'd have lunch at the peak. You said it was legendary!

CLAY: The peak is legendary.

AUGUST: And I packed bologna sandwiches.

JAMIE: Wait wait wait! We strained and struggled just to get to the top of a mound of dirt and look out at some water that – by the way – was a lot easier to see a few hours ago when we were NEXT TO IT, and, and, and eat bologna sandwiches?

KAI: Wow. You're really upset aren't you?

JAMIE: YES! ISN'T THAT OBVIOUS!? *(JAMIE looks around frantically.)* Now how, exactly, do we get down from here!? Where's the chair lift?

CLAY: Chair lift?

JAMIE: Oh man, don't tell me…. You want me to *hike* down!?

CLAY: Well, yeah. We're hiking.

JAMIE: You've got to be kidding me!

KAI: Sorry. It's the only way.

JAMIE: Okay, okay. I'll hike down, but when we check in to the spa, I want my own room far away from all of you. I've had enough. C'mon let's go before it gets dark.

> *(JAMIE exits. KAI, CLAY, and AUGUST look at each other.)*

KAI: What spa?

> *(CLAY and AUGUST shrug. They all exit)*

> *- END SCENE -*

LAST DAY OF SUMMER
(3 Actors)

(ALEX and CRIS knock on JACKI's front door.)

ALEX: Open up!

(JACKI answers the door. ALEX and CRIS are energetic and happy. JACKI is distressed and anxious.)

JACKI: What're you doing here?

CRIS: There's a wiffle ball tournament in Parker's backyard! Grab your sneakers! Let's go!

JACKI: Oh - ah. I can't. You go.

ALEX: Why not?

JACKI: I just can't. Sorry.

CRIS: You're the best hitter we got. You gotta come.

JACKI: No. It's - sorry. No. I'll see you tomorrow at school.

(JACKI tries to close the door. ALEX catches it.)

ALEX: Hey, wait. It's the last night of summer. We have to soak it in.

JACKI: I know. But -

CRIS: No more buts! Let's gooooo!

(Overwhelmed, JACKI yells in protest.)

JACKI: I CAN'T!

ALEX: Woah. You okay?

JACKI: Yes, I - no. Well, I don't know. I - I have a lot to do.

84

CRIS: It's summer. There's nothing to do.

(JACKI fidgets nervously and struggles to get their words out. As JACKI speaks, JACKI gets more and more anxious.)

JACKI: No. No. I have to organize my school supplies and do summer reading and and clean my room. The summer reading. It's long. I - It's a lot.

ALEX: Didn't you do that already?

JACKI: I have to re-read it and practice my Spanish. We have Spanish on Monday. Tomorrow. Tomorrow is Monday. The first day of school. Next year - it's a big year. It'll be different. I don't know. I've been in my room all day. Reading and re-reading. I haven't eaten. It won't - I can't remember - it's not working. I don't feel good. *(JACKI bends over in pain.)*

ALEX: Hey sit down.

(JACKI sits.)

JACKI: My chest. It feels like someone is inside my chest trying to break out.

ALEX: Just breathe. Relax.

JACKI: I can't. Relax. You don't understand.

CRIS: Okay. Then explain it to us.

JACKI: I can't. I can't do anything. I can't.

(JACKI curls up in a ball and rocks back and forth.)

ALEX: Then we won't do anything either.

CRIS: Yeah. We'll just sit with you.

(ALEX and CRIS sit on either side of JACKI.)

JACKI: No. No. Go. You'll miss your game.

ALEX: There will be other games.

JACKI: No - I - I -

CRIS: Hey, it's okay. I get nervous too.

JACKI: Not like this.

CRIS: We're different people. We worry differently. That's okay.

JACKI: I'm sorry.

ALEX: Stop apologizing. Last summer, I broke my ankle. You hung with me. Now we wanna hang with you.

CRIS: You'll be okay.

JACKI: I feel so bad.

ALEX: I know.

CRIS: You won't always feel like this.

ALEX: Let's just sit in the badness and let it pass.

CRIS: We'll just sit right here with you. And we'll let it pass. Together.

(They sit.)

- END SCENE -

THE INTERRUPTION
(4 Actors)

(SHAY runs into their Dad's office. SHAY stands downstage and looks out at the audience, speaking to their off-stage Dad, who remains unseen.)

SHAY: Dad! Have you seen my sneakers? *(SHAY realizes their Dad is on the phone.)* Oh, sorry. You're on a call. I won't - I'll stop. Sorry. Sorry. Bye.

(SHAY exits).

(A moment later, CLEO enters.)

CLEO: Dad! Shay took my sneakers! It's not fair! Those are my - who are you talking to? *(The off-stage dad explains he's talking to his boss.)* Oh, HI BOSS! Okay, okay, my bad. I'll go.

(CLEO exits.)

(A moment later, MEMPHIS and ARDEN enter.)

MEMPHIS: Shay and Cleo are fighting!

ARDEN: They aren't allowed to fight!

MEMPHIS: Yeah, yeah. We told 'em, but they won't listen to -

(The off-stage Dad says he's talking to his boss and needs to be left alone.)

ARDEN: Your boss? Oh! Whoops. All right. We'll get them to stop. Don't worry.

(MEMPHIS and ARDEN exit.)

(A moment later, SHAY, CLEO, and MEMPHIS enter.)

SHAY: Memphis just told us we're grounded!

CLEO *(to MEMPHIS)*: You can't ground us. Only a parent can ground us!

MEMPHIS: Dad, I told them I had your blessing. I have your blessing, right?!

> *(The off-stage Dad tells them they are not grounded, but they will be soon if they don't leave.)*

SHAY: Told you, Memphis!

MEMPHIS: Fine. Fine. We'll go! But I get to use your new iPad!

> *(MEMPHIS runs off-stage.)*

CLEO: Hey, that's mine!

> *(CLEO and SHAY chase MEMPHIS and run off-stage.)*

> *(A moment later, ARDEN enters.)*

ARDEN: Dad? Dad. Dad. Dad?! *(The off-stage Dad asks what ARDEN wants.)* I just wanted to say I'm gonna guard the door and keep them out. No more interruptions! *(ARDEN goes to the phone and yells into the receiver.)* Ms. Boss Lady?! Sorry. It won't happen again! And thanks for letting my Dad work from home. And it would be great if you gave him a promotion... and a raise. *(The off-stage Dad shoos ARDEN away.)* Okay, okay. I'm going! I got your back, Dad. No more interruptions. Promise.

> *(ARDEN exits)*

> *(ARDEN enters.)*

ARDEN: Hey, Dad? You're the best. Okay bye.

> *- END SCENE -*

YEARBOOK
(3 Actors)

(JUDE and PARKER sign yearbooks. INDY approaches them.)

INDY: Hey, will you two sign my yearbook?

JUDE: Sure!

(JUDE and PARKER sign.)

INDY: Thanks so much! I really appreciate it.

(They pass the yearbook back to INDY.)

PARKER: Here you go.

(INDY reads what they wrote.)

INDY: "Have a great summer. From, Jude"

PARKER: And I signed at the bottom there.

INDY: "Fun times in English class! Never change. Best, Parker"

JUDE: You wanna sign mine?

INDY: Hmmm...

PARKER: What's wrong?

INDY: Oh. Nothing.

JUDE: What?

INDY: Oh, it's just...I dunno. You don't want to maybe add a little more color?

JUDE: More color?

INDY: Yeah a little more spice, a bit more detail? Something to make it pop?

PARKER: You don't like what we wrote?

INDY: No, no, I like it. I just think it could use a little more oomph maybe?

JUDE: You want us to edit it?

INDY: Only if you want to.

JUDE: I mean, I guess I could add a little?

INDY: Great. Great. Yeah. Do that!

> *(INDY passes the yearbook back to JUDE and PARKER. They write while INDY watches closely.)*

INDY: Hmmmm...

PARKER: What?

INDY: Nothing. Nothing.

JUDE: Something wrong?

INDY: "You rock!" - That's a little generic, no?

PARKER: And what exactly would you recommend?

INDY: Maybe something about my sense of humor? Or my charisma?

JUDE: Huh?

INDY: Maybe something like "Indy you are beyond awesome!" or "Thanks for cracking me up in English class!"

PARKER: Okay...

> *(They write. INDY watches and offers feedback.)*

INDY: But with exclamation points! And maybe some bubble letters.

JUDE: How do you - ?

INDY: Here. Let me. *(INDY takes the yearbook and writes.)* Like this see? "Indy, You're the funnest kid in school!" "Indy, I'll miss you soooooo much!" Doesn't that look nice?

PARKER: Um. Yeah?

INDY: Great work, you two. Thanks so much!

JUDE: Uh, no problem.

INDY: Seriously. This is really too kind. You shouldn't have.

PARKER: Do you, uh, wanna sign ours now?

INDY: Aw shucks! Looks like my pen is outta ink. Maybe next time?

(INDY exits.)

- END SCENE -

GRADUATION
(3 Actors)

(WHITNEY, PARIS, and SANDY sit onstage at graduation. WHITNEY and PARIS look out at the audience and whisper to one another. SANDY sits beside them and listens.)

WHITNEY: How much longer?

PARIS: Not much longer. They're at the M's already.

WHITNEY: Wow. I can't believe it. In a few minutes, we're officially graduates.

PARIS: Is my hat on straight?

WHITNEY: Yeah, looks good to me.

PARIS: Thanks. *(PARIS looks over at the principal.)* Look at Principal Herrera. She looks sad.

WHITNEY: Makes sense. Saying goodbye is hard. It's a sad day.

SANDY *(Muttering)*: Sad?

WHITNEY: Did you say something?

SANDY: No - I - sorry. Didn't mean to.

PARIS: That's okay. You must be really upset about graduating, huh?

SANDY: Me?

PARIS: Yeah. You love this school. You're like obsessed with your classes. Every time I saw you, you were in the library studying, right?

SANDY: Oh. Yeah. I guess.

WHITNEY: I'm sure you'll like your classes in high school too though. Where are you going?

SANDY: August Prep.

PARIS: Impressive!

SANDY: Thanks.

WHITNEY: We're going to Southfield High.

SANDY: Nice.

PARIS: Don't worry. I bet August Prep has a nice library too.

SANDY: I... Well, I don't like really love the library or anything...

WHITNEY: Then why were you always in there?

SANDY: Well... um, it's just... nobody would really talk to me at lunch.

WHITNEY: What? That's not true.

PARIS: You could have sat with us.

SANDY: I - well - I tried to sit with you a few years back.

PARIS: You did? When?

SANDY: On my first day.

WHITNEY: I don't remember that.

PARIS: They're at the R's! We gotta get up.

> *(They stand up and get in line to collect their diplomas.)*

SANDY: It didn't seem like you wanted me around.

WHITNEY: Wait. Really?

PARIS: Honestly, I thought you didn't like *us*.

WHITNEY: I always figured you thought we weren't smart enough or something.

93

SANDY: What!? No way.

PARIS: Then why didn't you talk to us? You were always keeping to yourself.

SANDY: That's just because you didn't talk to me.

WHITNEY: Oh. Well. I guess we should have.

PARIS: Sorry.

SANDY: I - I guess I'm sorry too.

- END SCENE -

THE FINAL PAGE
(3 Actors)

(Three siblings in their bedroom. JODY reads aloud to LOU and NICO.)

JODY: "Morris reported that the violin case was found in a sarcophagus last week. A trumpet case was found two days later -"

(JODY turns the page and stops reading.)

LOU: Why'd you stop?

JODY: We're almost done. This is the last page.

NICO: Ah! I'm so excited to see how it ends!

JODY: But, I just realized – this may be the best book I've ever read.

NICO: Well, yeah. Me too.

LOU: Definitely. So?

JODY: So, I don't want it to be over. It's too sad.

LOU: After over a hundred and fifty pages and weeks of reading, you want to stop now?

NICO: We can always read it again once we finish.

JODY: But we'll never do it for the first time again, right? All of the surprises and the suspense. The fun. The moment will pass and we won't get it back.

LOU: Well, I guess that's true.

NICO: That *is* sad. I guess we could just stop reading?

LOU: And never finish it?

JODY: Well that doesn't sound great either.

NICO: So what then?

LOU: We can't suspend time, right? We have to keep going forward.

JODY: But who knows what's next? It may never be this good again.

LOU: I guess that's kinda the fun part. The not knowing. That's the adventure of it all.

NICO: I'll miss it though.

LOU: Yeah.

JODY: Me too.

NICO: So... should we keep reading?

LOU: I think we should.

JODY: Okay. Where was I? "Morris reported - "

(JODY stops, puts the book down.)

LOU: Hey, it's okay. We can take our time. Let's savor it. We'll take turns. We'll each read a line.

NICO: That sounds good.

JODY: Yeah that's better. Thanks.

LOU: Ready?

JODY: Ready.

NICO: Ready.

LOU: Final page. Let's go.

- END SCENE -

About the Author

JESSICA PENZIAS is an award-winning librettist and playwright. Her works include the Beat by Beat musical *BOTS!* (with Denver Casado and Christyn Budzyna), *The Prince's New Pet* (with Anthony De Angelis and Christyn Budzyna), *From The Mixed-Up Files of Mrs. Basil E. Frankweiler* (with Adam Ben-David and Christyn Budzyna), *The Fox Sisters* (with De Angelis and Budzyna), *Dime A Dozen*, and *The Whole Damn Thing.*

Jessica is a proud member of the Dramatists Guild of America, the Tony Award-honored BMI Lehman Engel Musical Theatre Librettists' Workshop, and the 92Y Musical Theater Development Lab. She was awarded the Jerry Harrington Award For Outstanding Creative Achievement in 2016. As an associate at Jill Furman Productions, Jessica aided in the development and production of *Hamilton* and *Rodgers and Hammerstein's Cinderella.* She holds a degree in creative writing and theatre arts from the University of Pennsylvania. You can visit her website at JessicaPenzias.com.

Made in United States
Troutdale, OR
01/12/2024